KING ST.

Set One
BOOK I

Sam and Jim

Sam and Jim
King Street: Readers Set One - Book 1
Copyright © Iris Nunn 2014

Text: Iris Nunn
Editor: June Lewis
Illustrations: Pip Jones and Marta Kwasniewska

Published in 2014 by Gatehouse Media Limited. Reprinted in 2018.

ISBN: 978-1-84231-106-6

British Library Cataloguing-in-Publication Data:
A catalogue record for this book is available from the British Library

I am Sam.

I live at number ten.

I was a dustman.

I have a bad leg.

I am sixty-six.

This is Jim.

He is a black labrador.

He is my dog.

He is my pal.